HERCULES' 11TH LABOR

PANDORA'S BOX

DEMETER AND PERSEPHONE

THREE MYTHS FROM ANCIENT GREECE

retold by Carol Pugliano-Martin

Table of Contents

MYTHS

What is a myth?

A myth (MITH) is a story that explains something that occurs in nature. It might tell how the world began or explain why the world is the way it is. The main character in a myth is usually a god or goddess or a hero with special powers. Sometimes the hero in a myth is on a quest (KWEST), a journey in search of adventure.

What is the purpose of a myth?

Long ago, people believed myths to be true. They relied on these stories to explain events they did not understand, like violent storms or why there is night and day. Today, myths help us see what events confused or interested people long ago. The explanations in myths are creative and fun. They are exciting, too.

How do you read a myth?

The title of a myth often tells what event in nature the myth explains. Think about how the event is explained when you read a myth. Look for a hero with extraordinary powers. Ask yourself, *What does this hero do? How do the hero's actions help explain an event?*

Homer

Features of a Myth

Myths often take place before time, or recorded history as we know it, began.

Myths have characters that are humans, or humanlike, and experience human emotions.

Myths have gods, goddesses, heroes, and fantastic creatures with supernatural powers.

Myths often explain the origins of the world and its creatures.

Myths often explain the worldview of a people or culture and may have religious elements.

Characters often perform heroic tasks or go on quests.

Who invented myths?

In ancient times, storytellers told myths to answer questions about the world. Their listeners understood the heroes of these myths. They were heroes with human qualities similar to their own, but their super powers meant that they could perform amazing deeds. In an ancient Greek myth, the god Prometheus gives humans the gift of fire. In another myth, the Greek goddess Demeter explains the change of seasons. The Mexican god Quetzalcoatl takes a dangerous journey to his homeland in a myth. As the centuries passed, these stories were told and retold and then written down. Today science has explained the events in myths, but readers still enjoy the exciting adventures of these heroes.

TOOLS FOR READERS AND WRITERS

Word Choice

Writers choose their words very carefully. Their goal is to have readers see, hear, and feel what they see, hear, and feel. With the right word choice, readers "get inside" the mind of the writer and see things in a new way. Writers are always looking for the "just right" word to help a reader appreciate and agree with their points of view and think about a specific image or feeling as they do.

Prefixes

Good writers use as few words as possible to convey meaning. One way to do this is with prefixes. When these small parts of words are put in front of a root or base word, the meaning of that word changes. For example, the prefixes **im-** and **in-** mean "not." Instead of saying "not mature," authors say "immature." Instead of saying "not visible," authors say "invisible."

Cause-and-Effect Relationships

One way writers explain information is to tell why certain events happen. When they write about an event, they often discuss the causes and effects of those events. Good readers pay attention to what happens and to explanations of why they happened. Identifying each event as the effect and the reason for it as the cause helps readers better understand the text.

MEET SOME MYTHIC FIGURES
HERCULES

Hercules is the Roman name for the Greek hero-god Heracles. He was son of Zeus, king of the Greek gods, and a mortal woman named Alcmene. Zeus's wife, the goddess Hera, was furious with Zeus and Alcmene for this betrayal, and she plotted to kill the baby Hercules. However, because of Hercules' status as half-god, he was imbued with superhuman strength. All of Hera's plans to destroy him failed.

Hercules grew up and became a powerful, heroic figure who performed many amazing feats over many years. He married and had children. But Hera, still wishing to punish Hercules, put a spell on him that caused Hercules to go insane temporarily and kill his wife and children. In order to pay for this horrible crime, Hercules was ordered to become a slave of Eurystheus, king of Mycenae, and perform a dozen difficult and dangerous physical challenges, called labors, to cleanse him of his crime. These labors included slaying a lion; conquering the many-headed sea serpent, the Hydra; taming man-eating horses; and the tale in this book: retrieving Hera's golden apples.

Hercules eventually completed all twelve of his labors and gained his freedom. After a life of further adventures, he died and then became immortal, living on Mount Olympus with the other Greek gods and goddesses.

PANDORA

Zeus gave two Titans the task of creating creatures to populate Earth. Epimetheus created the mammals, birds, insects, and fish of the world. Prometheus created man. Epimetheus then gave his creations fur, feathers, tails, and scales. Prometheus needed to give his new mortals more. He thought and thought and finally arrived at the perfect gift— fire! Although Zeus had declared that fire belonged to the gods, Prometheus felt that fire should be shared with the mortals. He stole fire from Mount Olympus, Zeus's home, and gave it to the mortals.

When Zeus discovered this betrayal, he gave a terrible punishment to Prometheus. Prometheus was tied to the side of a mountain while large birds pecked out his liver. Prometheus's liver grew back each day and the cycle repeated itself over and over. It was an awful fate for poor Prometheus.

So, Prometheus was punished for giving fire. Now the mortals must be punished for receiving it. And that punishment was concealed as a beautiful but curious woman named Pandora.

DEMETER AND PERSEPHONE

Many cultures have myths that explain how the seasons came to be. The story of Demeter and Persephone is the ancient Greek telling of that event. Zeus controls all things on Earth and above. His brother, Hades, rules the Underworld, the place where people go after they die. Their other brother, Poseidon, rules the sea.

Zeus's other siblings control specialized areas. For instance, Zeus's sister Demeter is the goddess of the harvest. She watches over the fields, crops, trees, and flowers of the world. Demeter was totally devoted to her daughter Persephone and couldn't bear to be without her. This explains the complete despair that Demeter felt when her beloved Persephone was taken from her by Hades, and her utter joy at having Persephone returned to her.

The number of months that Persephone is in the Underworld varies depending on the retelling of the myth, probably because winter, the period when the crops and trees are barren, differs depending on geographic location. Some versions have her eating six pomegranate seeds, others four, and others do not mention a specific number.

HERCULES' 11TH LABOR: THE GOLDEN APPLES

Hercules has just returned from performing his grueling tenth labor for King Eurystheus. He defeated the giant Geryon and captured his cattle. Though exhausted, Hercules gets his next assignment.

"Bring me some of Hera's golden apples," roared King Eurystheus. "They were a wedding gift for her from Zeus and will make anyone who eats them **immortal**."

"But you know I am an enemy of Hera," said Hercules.

"She will never allow me to have any of those apples. Surely this task is **impossible**!"

King Eurystheus looked smug. "Impossible for the great Hercules?"

"Of course not! It's just that no mortal can enter Hera's garden. The apples are guarded by the Hesperides, daughters of the Titan Atlas," said Hercules hesitantly. "Not to mention the fierce, many-headed dragon Ladon."

Eurystheus looked victorious. "Are you admitting defeat? Willing to remain my slave forever?"

"Never!" shouted Hercules. Then he hung his head. "I will do as you ask."

So Hercules set off for the garden at the western edge of the world where the apples grew. On the way, he encountered many obstacles and conquered several enemies. He came upon Prometheus chained to a mountain and attacked daily by an eagle.

"Hercules," cried Prometheus, who was at that moment being ravaged by the mighty bird. "Please help me. Rid me of this agony!"

"I will help you, Prometheus," said Hercules, and he slew the eagle who caused Prometheus such pain.

"I am forever in your debt," said Prometheus. "To show you my gratitude, Hercules, I will tell you how you may accomplish your eleventh labor, for I have heard that you must steal Hera's golden apples for King Eurystheus."

"Tell me, please," said Hercules, "for I am quite daunted by this task."

"Go to Atlas," whispered Prometheus, for he did not want the gods to hear him helping Hercules. "His daughters, the nymphs who guard the apples, will surely give some of the golden fruit to their own father."

"Ah, true. But what of the dragon, Ladon?" asked Hercules.

"An archer of your expertise should be able to **immobilize** that beast with one arrow shot over the wall."

Hercules thanked Prometheus for the advice and headed pell-mell across the mountains. He soon found himself face to face with the strained expression of the giant Atlas, whose burden was to hold up the heavens on a pillar on his shoulders.

"Hercules! What . . . brings . . . you . . . here?" asked Atlas as he struggled under the heavy weight.

"I have come to ask for your help," said Hercules, "for you are immortal and the favor I ask is great."

"What is it then?" grunted Atlas.

"As you know, I have been sentenced to perform twelve labors for King Eurystheus," said Hercules. "Indeed, they have

This marble sculpture from Greece in the fifth century B.C.E. shows Heracles holding up the sky.

been quite a challenge. Now I am up to my eleventh labor, which is to bring some of Hera's golden apples to the king."

Atlas chuckled through his grimace. "This will be your most difficult task yet. The apples are guarded by the dreaded dragon Ladon as well as my darling daughters."

"I am aware of that," said Hercules. "I believe I can slay the dragon. But your daughters will be loyal to Hera and will never allow me entry into the garden. You, however, their father, will be able to persuade them."

"But Hercules, as you see, I am like you in that I am also being punished. I have fought against Zeus and now I must hold up the heavens for all eternity," said the tired Titan. "I cannot leave my post here, though it has become such a burden to me."

Hercules thought for a moment.

"I am strong, Atlas. I will take up your burden while you fetch the apples for me," said Hercules.

The thought of being relieved from his burden appealed greatly to Atlas, for he had been suffering for as long as he could remember. Then the glimmer of an idea slowly began to take shape in his brain. Once Hercules was holding up the heavens, Atlas would leave him there with the burden that had been given to him—and he would be free.

"Well, Hercules," said Atlas craftily, "I would be glad to help you. Please take my place while I get the apples for you."

"First, I will slay the dragon," said Hercules, and he headed off toward the garden. As Prometheus had advised, the task was completed with a single shot of an arrow over the garden wall.

"That deed is done," said Hercules as he returned to Atlas. "And now I will fulfill my end of the bargain I made with you."

And with that, Hercules took Atlas's place. He held up the heavens while Atlas set off to get the apples for Hercules.

Despite his great strength, Hercules struggled miserably. "Oh! I hope Atlas returns soon, for the weight is almost more than even I can bear!" he said. Five minutes passed, then ten. Hercules waited and waited. The wait seemed **interminable**. How would Hercules hold on any longer?

Atlas returned not a moment too soon, for Hercules' knees buckled under the enormous weight. "I have brought your apples," said Atlas.

"Thank you, Atlas," said a relieved Hercules. "And now, please replace me under this pillar."

A devious smile curled on Atlas's lips. "There's been a change of plans. I have decided that I no longer wish to hold up the heavens. You must now do it for me!" said Atlas, chuckling.

"You tricked me!" thundered Hercules. "And I trusted you!"

"That was your mistake," said Atlas. "I will not return to such a harsh punishment."

Hercules reflected on his situation, sweat beading down his furrowed brow. Then his eyes brightened with an idea. His tone softened as he spoke to Atlas again.

"I understand, Atlas," said Hercules. "You are a clever opponent, too clever for me. I will continue to hold up the heavens. But my shoulders are so sore. Please, hold the pillar for just one moment more while I go get a cushion for my weary shoulders."

"I have been in your position, Hercules. I guess I can allow you that little luxury." The triumphant Atlas handed the golden apples to Hercules and took up the weight of the world once more as Hercules hurried off to find a cushion.

Ten minutes passed, then twenty. Atlas waited and waited for Hercules to return. "Hercules! Haven't you gotten that cushion yet?" he bellowed. But there was no answer from Hercules.

"Hercules? Hercules?!" called out the bewildered Titan. But Hercules never came back to take the weight off Atlas's weary shoulders. Rather, he returned Atlas's trick with a trick of his own.

Soon thereafter, Hercules delivered the golden apples to King Eurystheus, who was quite surprised that once again, Hercules had completed a seemingly impossible task.

"You are a formidable figure indeed, Hercules," mused Eurystheus, as he collected the golden apples. "Indeed."

A brief, awkward silence followed. Then Hercules, standing proudly before the king, said, "I await word of my twelfth and final labor."

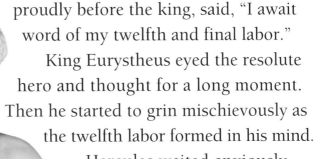

King Eurystheus eyed the resolute hero and thought for a long moment. Then he started to grin mischievously as the twelfth labor formed in his mind. Hercules waited anxiously, though eagerly, for his next, and final, adventure.

Analyze the Characters and Plot

- Who are the main characters in the myth?
- Who are the minor characters in the myth?
- What is Hercules' eleventh challenge?
- What challenges does he conquer while completing the eleventh challenge?
- How does Atlas trick Hercules? How does Hercules trick Atlas?
- How does the myth end?

Prometheus

Focus on Comprehension: Evaluate Cause-and-Effect Relationships

- Why is Hercules hesitant about bringing Hera's golden apples to King Eurystheus?
- Why does Hercules go to Atlas for help?
- King Eurystheus gives Hercules a task that the king thinks is too difficult to perform. What effect does Hercules' completion of the task have on King Eurystheus?

Analyze the Tools Writers Use: Word Choice

- On page 9, the author says that Eurystheus "looked victorious." What do you think his face looked like? Did he have a huge smile? Did he have a smug smile?
- On page 9, the author says Prometheus "was being ravaged by the mighty bird." What do you think Prometheus looked like after being ravaged by the bird? What do you think the bird looked like while it was ravaging Prometheus?
- On page 11, the author says that "the glimmer of an idea" took shape in Atlas's brain. What does the author mean by this? What is the glimmer of an idea? How can it turn into action?
- On page 12, the author says "a devious smile curled on Atlas's lips." What does a devious smile look like?

Focus on Words: Prefixes (im-, in-)

Make a chart like the one below. Read each word in the chart. For each word, identify its part of speech as it is used in the myth. Then identify the word's prefix and the prefix's meaning. Finally, explain how the prefix changes the meaning of the base word.

Page	Word	Part of Speech	Prefix and Its Meaning	How Prefix Changes Meaning of Base Word
8	immortal			
9	impossible			
10	immobilize			
12	interminable			

PANDORA'S BOX

*Picture, if you will, a time when there was no pain. A time when there was no sadness. Even a time when there was no death. There was such a time. But that was long ago, before an **incessantly** curious girl named Pandora made a small move that would change the world in a very big way—forever.*

Zeus, the king of the gods, wanted a perfect gift for Epimetheus, who had won his favor by creating the animals that populated the world.

"A wife will be just the thing for my son," decreed Zeus. And he went to the other gods to request their help in creating the perfect woman for his son. Aphrodite, the goddess of love, gave her beauty. Apollo, the god of music, gave her musical talent. Hestia, the goddess of hearth and home, gave her a gentle soul. And, lastly, Athena, the goddess of wisdom, bestowed upon the woman a keen desire to know all things. And Zeus named the woman Pandora.

But Zeus was a vengeful god and he always had a master plan lurking beneath all he did. Zeus had already punished his other son, Prometheus, who had gone against his wishes and given fire to humans. Fire was a power reserved for the gods! Humans needed to be punished, too, for accepting fire.

So, along with the gift of Pandora, Zeus gave Epimetheus a beautiful box as a wedding gift. It was an unusual wedding gift, with an even odder warning: "You must never, ever open this box, under any circumstances," commanded Zeus.

Pandora stared and stared at the box. She was intrigued. Her desire to know all things nearly **incapacitated** her. "Whatever can be in it and why can't I open it?" she asked Epimetheus.

"I don't know, but since father Zeus has willed it, then it must be so," said Epimetheus. "Do not open it, Pandora!"

But Pandora could not get that box off her mind. Whenever she walked by the box, her fingers itched to open it.

"Put it out of your mind, Pandora," warned Epimetheus.

Oh, how Pandora tried! She worked hard to convince herself that there was nothing special in the box.

It's probably just some linens or dishes, she thought. *But then why couldn't we open it? No, it must be something wonderful, something gloriously special and precious for it to be treated as such a mystery.*

Pandora could not conceal her curiosity from her husband, who caught her stroking the lid of the box. "Pandora!" scolded Epimetheus. "Zeus's resolve is **impenetrable**, his wrath **infinite**! He has commanded us not to open the box and we will not!"

One day, Epimetheus was away and all Pandora could think about was opening the box. She was very much like a child who, when specifically told she cannot do something, wants to do it all the more.

If no one is here to watch me, she thought, *then no one will know I disobeyed Zeus.* Pandora inched toward the box. The closer she got, the more curious she became. She was drawn to the box like steel to a magnet.

"I don't have to open the box all the way," Pandora said

softly to herself as she reached toward the box, "just enough to take a quick peek. Then I'll close the latch, my curiosity will be satisfied, and I can finally go on with my life."

By now, Pandora's fingers were touching the latch that held the box shut. There was no stopping her now. She slowly lifted the latch and opened the top of the box. Suddenly, an icy wind blew through the room; its force knocked her to the ground. Out of the box flew several slimy, snarling, and very ugly creatures. Pandora was stricken with fear.

"I am Disease!" moaned one of the creatures.

"I am Pain!" shrieked another.

"I am Jealousy!" whined a third.

Pandora could not stand the piercing, shrill noises the creatures emitted. She put her hands over her ears, but nothing could stop the din as Death, Old Age, Disappointment, Cruelty, and Hate also flew out of the box.

Pandora leaped to her feet, ran to the box, and shut the lid tightly as the miseries giddily flew out the window, ready to spread themselves among the mortals who had wronged Zeus by accepting the gift of fire.

"Ah, thank goodness," spoke a kind, **innocuous**-sounding voice.

"Oh no, there are more of you?" wailed Pandora.

"I am not one of them," said the calm voice. "I am Hope. By leaving me in the box, you are making sure that despite all of the new miseries unleashed in the world, hope remains to ease human beings' suffering and pain."

So now, although mankind suffers from countless miseries, as long as Pandora keeps Hope in the box, man can keep hope alive.

Analyze the Characters and Plot
- Who are the main characters in the myth?
- Who are the minor characters in the myth?
- What word describes Pandora?
- What word describes Epimetheus?
- What happens after Pandora opens the box?
- What happens at the end of the myth?

Focus on Comprehension:
Evaluate Cause-and-Effect Relationships
- Zeus gives Epimetheus a wife because . . .
- Why does Zeus want to punish humans?
- Epimetheus will not open the box because . . .
- Because Pandora opens the box . . .

Focus on Character Motive
The author says that Zeus was a vengeful god. He was angry with Prometheus for giving fire to humans, and he was angry with the humans for accepting the gift of fire from Prometheus. For this infraction, he punished Prometheus. The author also says that Zeus always had a master plan lurking behind all that he did. In other words, he had an ulterior motive. He was looking for a way to punish the humans.
- After reading the story and thinking about Zeus's ulterior motive, what character trait did Zeus want Pandora to have?
- What might have happened if Pandora had not opened the box?

Analyze the Tools Writers Use: Word Choice

• On page 17, Epimetheus tells Pandora to "Put it out of your mind." What does Epimetheus mean by these words?

• On page 17, the author says that Pandora was stroking the lid of the box. What might this scene have looked like?

• On page 17, Epimetheus says that "Zeus's resolve is impenetrable, his wrath infinite." What do these words say about Zeus?

• On page 18, the author says that Pandora is "drawn to the box like steel to a magnet." What do these words imply about Pandora's feelings at the time?

Focus on Words: Prefixes (im-, in-)

Make a chart like the one below. Read each word in the chart. For each word, identify its part of speech as it is used in the myth. Then identify the word's prefix and the prefix's meaning. Finally, explain how the prefix changes the meaning of the base word.

Page	Word	Part of Speech	Prefix and Its Meaning	How Prefix Changes Meaning of Base Word
16	incessantly			
17	incapacitated			
17	impenetrable			
17	infinite			
19	innocuous			

DEMETER AND PERSEPHONE

Outside, snow blankets the fields. A cold wind blows the empty tree branches. Nothing grows. Everything waits. It wasn't always like this. Long ago, people harvested nature's bounty year-round. The sun was bright and warm and Earth was full of flowers. But all that changed when a mother got revenge for an injustice done to her daughter.

Demeter, goddess of the harvest, sat under the shade of a tree as she watched her daughter Persephone pick flowers in the field. *My beautiful child is truly my greatest joy in the world*, she thought happily as Persephone, now a comely young woman, frolicked with some nymphs. *Surely I would be* **inconsolable** *without her.*

Meanwhile, down in the Underworld, Hades, the god of that dark land, was not so happy. "I am lonely! I must have a bride!" he raged.

But what woman would want to marry such a brooding, unhappy man? Hades knew that if he wanted a wife, he was going to have to take one by force.

Hades boarded his black chariot and whipped his giant black stallions toward the fields above his realm. As soon as the chariot, horses, and

Since this is a myth, the author sets the time of the story "long ago."

In the opening paragraph, the author establishes the strong emotional bond between Demeter and Persephone that propels, or moves forward, the story line.

The author introduces the villain of the story, Hades. Although he is a god, the author gives him human feelings—loneliness and sadness—and a motivation for his actions.

driver burst through the ground, Hades's eyes alighted upon the lovely Persephone.

A beautiful girl like that could brighten up my gloomy home, thought Hades. *She will be my wife!* Hades knew that Persephone was Demeter's daughter. *Demeter watches her very carefully. I will have to wait until just the right moment to steal her away.*

Demeter beamed contentedly as she watched Persephone and the nymphs gambol through the tall grasses.

the Underworld

A warm wind rustled through the green leaves and Demeter drifted off to sleep with a smile on her face.

"Now is my chance!" shouted Hades. Lashing his stallions, he raced toward Persephone. "I've got you!" Hades exclaimed as he scooped up Persephone and plopped her into his chariot.

"Help me, Mother!" cried Persephone.

The author develops the plot: Hades kidnaps Persephone. She is in jeopardy— a difficult spot. Readers will want to find out what will happen to her and what Demeter will do.

But Hades's stallions were too fast; they disappeared into the earth and made their way down to the Underworld even before Demeter could open her eyes.

When she awoke, Demeter searched the fields, the brook, and the woods for her darling daughter. "Persephone! Persephone! It's time to go home," she called with increasing anguish. She searched for several days to no avail.

Something unusual was happening to Earth as Demeter searched. The leaves of the trees turned brown and fell to the ground. The plants and flowers wilted and died. Demeter could only concentrate on finding Persephone. Too filled with sorrow, she had no energy to devote to caring for Earth.

Meanwhile, things were equally bleak in the Underworld.

"Please eat, my dear, you must keep up your strength," Hades cajoled Persephone.

"No! I want my mother! I want to go home!" Persephone cried.

"Give it time, Persephone. In time, you will come to love it here and love me."

"Never!" shouted Persephone and she wailed in grief.

Persephone

By this time, Demeter was frantic with worry. She decided to ask the sun god, Helios, if he had seen anything.

"Ah, yes, I have," said Helios solemnly. "Hades has taken Persephone to the Underworld."

"Who could have allowed this? How could this happen?" Demeter shrieked.

"Zeus is the only one who can answer that question," said Helios.

So Demeter made her way up to Mount Olympus. "Zeus! Hades has stolen my daughter! Did you know anything about this?"

"Alas, I did not. Sometimes my brother Hades does things behind my back," said Zeus. "But what he did was wrong."

"We must do something!" shouted Demeter.

"We will go and confront him. But it may be too late. If Persephone has eaten anything in the Underworld, the law states that she must stay there."

And so they headed to Hades's realm.

Persephone, who was naive and **innocent**, did not know the law of the Underworld. After days without eating, she had gotten very hungry. Hades was persuasive, so she agreed to nibble four seeds from the juicy pomegranate Hades offered her. She was too overcome with grief to eat any more. Only when she saw Demeter enter the dark realm did her mood brighten.

The author brings in a new character, Helios, to provide a piece of key information that moves the plot forward.

From this piece of information, which the author presents via Zeus's dialogue, readers now learn that Persephone's problem has worsened considerably. She may be trapped in the Underworld for eternity!

Myths are filled with adventure. Zeus and Demeter go into the dark, dangerous Underworld.

"Mother, oh Mother!"

"My beloved daughter! You're coming with me!" Demeter shouted.

"I'm afraid not," said the **implacable** Hades, "for Persephone has eaten my food."

"Is it true, dear child?" Demeter asked.

"Why, yes, but only four tiny pomegranate seeds."

"That's barely enough to keep a hummingbird humming, much less keep a young woman down here forever," said Zeus.

"You know the rules, my brother," said Hades, a grin contorting his normally dour face.

"Hades, be reasonable!" cried Demeter.

"Please, Hades," pleaded Persephone.

Hades looked longingly into Persephone's beautiful, though doleful, eyes and paused a long moment. His twisted smile lapsed back into a frown. "Brother, a word," he said.

Hades and Zeus huddled in a corner, whispering. After a brief deliberation, Zeus said, "We have come up with a compromise. Since Persephone has eaten four seeds, she will stay down in the Underworld with Hades for four months of the year."

Zeus, king of the gods, uses his wisdom to solve Persephone's problem.

"Four months!" cried Demeter. "No! I wouldn't be able to stand it. My grief will be **insurmountable**!"

"It's okay, Mother, really it is," said Persephone. "To tell the truth, Hades has treated me kindly. Four months will go by quickly and then you and I will be together again."

"It's the best I can do, Demeter," said Zeus.

"All right," said Demeter. "But during those four months, I will need to rest from my duties tending Earth, as my loneliness will be too much to bear. For those four months, nothing will grow or be harvested. Earth will reflect my feelings and become cold and barren. Only when my daughter and I are reunited will I radiate with the warmth of a mother's joy, and only then will Earth bloom again."

Note that the ancient Greeks told this myth to explain an element of nature: why we have winter.

And so it became then, and so it is now. When the air grows cold and snow falls and plants die and living things sleep, Persephone is with Hades in the Underworld. Only when she returns to Demeter does this mother of Earth bask in her joy and allow a warm sun to let other beautiful things grow once again.

In this painting, *The Return of Persephone*, the god Hermes brings Persephone to Demeter.

27

Analyze the Characters and Plot

- Who are the main characters in the myth?
- Who are the minor characters in the myth?
- Describe the relationship between Demeter and Persephone.
- What happens to Earth after Persephone is taken?
- What problem does Persephone face once she eats the pomegranate seeds?
- What happens at the end of the myth?

Focus on Comprehension:
Evaluate Cause-and-Effect Relationships

- Why does Hades think he will have to take a wife by force?
- Why does Hades choose Persephone as his wife?
- Why does Demeter talk to Zeus?
- Why does Persephone have to live with Hades for four months out of every year?

Demeter, goddess of the harvest

Analyze the Tools Writers Use: Word Choice

- Hades is not only an unhappy man—he is also a mean man. Identify examples that help you understand this character trait in Hades.

- On page 23, the author says that Hades's black chariot and black horses "burst through the ground." What do you think the author wants the reader to visualize by using these words?

- On page 25, Zeus says that Hades "does things behind my back." What does Zeus mean by this?

- On page 26, Demeter says that her "grief will be insurmountable" if Persephone has to live with Hades four months out of each year. Does this mean that Demeter will be a little sad or extremely sad?

Focus on Words: Prefixes (im-, in-)

Make a chart like the one below. Read each word in the chart. For each word, identify its part of speech as it is used in the myth. Then identify the word's prefix and the prefix's meaning. Finally, explain how the prefix changes the meaning of the base word.

Page	Word	Part of Speech	Prefix and Its Meaning	How Prefix Changes Meaning of Base Word
22	inconsolable			
25	innocent			
26	implacable			
26	insurmountable			

How does an author write a
MYTH?

Reread "Demeter and Persephone" and think about what Carol Pugliano-Martin did to retell this myth. How did she develop the story? How can you, as a writer, develop your own retelling of a myth?

1. Research Myths and Decide on One to Retell

Many cultures have their own myths and gods. First, decide on the culture whose myths you want to research. You may want to focus on one particular god or hero you already know about. Writers learn as much as they can about the myth they want to retell and often read different versions in books or from online sources. While you read the different versions of the myth, think about which parts you will retell and which parts you will leave out.

Character	Type of God	Traits/ Emotions	Examples
Demeter	goddess of the harvest	joy, upset, determined	she delights in watching her daughter; is very worried when she can't find her; loses all interest in caring for Earth; gets Zeus to help her confront Hades
Persephone	daughter of Demeter; goddess of spring; queen of the Underworld	happy, innocent, relieved, fair	she plays with nymphs; eats four pomegranate seeds without realizing the consequences; is delighted to see her mother come to her aid; agrees to stay with Hades
Hades	god of the Underworld	lonely, selfish, devious, willing to compromise	he is unhappy living alone in the Underworld; sees Persephone on Earth and steals her away; shows compassion and sets her free for eight months of the year

2. Identify and Brainstorm Characters

Writers ask these questions:

- Who are the major and minor characters in this myth?
- What type of god or hero? What special skills does he or she have?
- What human traits or emotions does each character possess?
- What words can I choose to develop the characters' traits?
- How will character traits affect the plot?

3. Rethink the Setting and Plot

Myths, like other fiction stories, have a setting and a plot. When you write a retelling of a myth, you have to be familiar with where and when the original story takes place, the problem and events of the story, and the solution to the problem. Then you can choose your own words in the retelling.

Demeter

Setting	ancient Greece
Problem of the Story	Hades, god of the Underworld, is lonely.
Story Events	1. Hades steals away Persephone. 2. Demeter searches for her, can't find her, grows worried, and asks the god Helios if he knows anything. 3. Helios tells Demeter about Hades; she goes to Zeus for help. 4. Zeus and Demeter travel to the Underworld to rescue Persephone. 5. While Persephone is in the Underworld, Hades gets her to eat four pomegranate seeds. Because she eats food there, she is now committed to staying there forever. 6. Demeter and Zeus plead with Hades to reconsider.
Solution to the Problem	Persephone will stay with Hades for four months of the year, during which time Demeter will be too sad to care for Earth. (These months are what we call winter.) During the other eight months, Persephone will be back with Demeter, and Demeter will be happy. (These are the seasons of spring, summer, and fall.)

GLOSSARY

immobilize   (ih-MOH-bih-lize) prevent from moving (page 10)

immortal   (ih-MOR-tul) exempt from death (page 8)

impenetrable   (im-PEH-neh-truh-bul) incapable of being penetrated or pierced (page 17)

implacable   (im-PLA-kuh-bul) not able to be appeased (page 26)

impossible   (im-PAH-sih-bul) extremely difficult or incapable of being done (page 9)

incapacitated   (in-kuh-PA-sih-tay-ted) disabled (page 17)

incessantly   (in-SEH-sent-lee) unceasingly (page 16)

inconsolable   (in-kun-SOH-luh-bul) incapable of feeling comfort (page 22)

infinite   (IN-fih-nit) endless (page 17)

innocent   (IH-nuh-sent) not guilty; blameless (page 25)

innocuous   (ih-NAH-kyoo-us) harmless (page 19)

insurmountable   (in-ser-MOWN-tuh-bul) unable to overcome (page 26)

interminable   (in-TER-mih-nuh-bul) seeming to have no end (page 12)